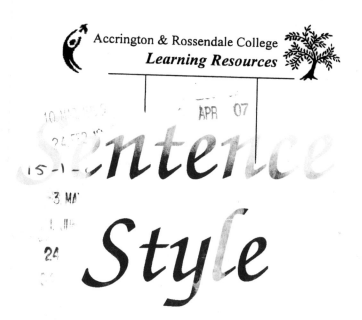

Sentence Style

Catherine Hilton

Margaret Hyder

MCH Publications

Contents

Introduction

The materials

These photocopiable materials are designed for:
- young people in Years 10, 11, 12 or 13;
- 16 -19 year old college students;
- adults in education, training or work.

The materials are sufficiently flexible to be used in a variety of learning situations: class/group sessions; open or distance learning.

Tutor information

This book is the second book in a series designed to help students to write and punctuate sentences. *'Sentence Style'* shows students how to: extend sentences by adding words and phrases to make their writing more interesting, descriptive or precise; combine sentences in a variety of ways. Throughout the worksheets, students are encouraged to check first drafts of their writing and find ways of improving their sentence style.

Although each worksheet is freestanding, they are arranged in developmental order and some students may need to access the sheets sequentially. The first worksheet, *'Check out your sentences'*, allows students to assess their knowledge about and confidence in writing in sentences. The second worksheet, *'Building on the foundations'*, summarises the points about simple sentences and introduces students to the ideas developed in *'Sentence Style'*.

Each worksheet deals with a specific topic and provides examples, guidance and practice. 'Reviews' summarise the concepts which have been developed in the worksheet. Answers or model answers are provided wherever appropriate. Where students are asked to produce their own sentences, they are told to discuss their writing with their tutors.

Tutors should encourage students to build up a portfolio of worksheets together with the *'Student guide'* to use as a reference source.

We have tried to avoid using terms with which students may be unfamiliar, however as this is not always possible, in the *'Student guide'* we provide a glossary of terms.

Photocopying

The worksheets may be photocopied provided they are used solely in your own institution. If you wish to photocopy for any other purpose, you must gain permission from *MCH Publications*.

© 1997 *MCH Publications*
ISBN 1 898901 14 7

Published by *MCH Publications*, PO Box No. 3720, Redditch, Worcestershire, B97 5EF.
Cover design by Vivienne Weatherill Oddy.
Printed by Bloomfield Ltd, 7b Waterloo Industrial Estate, Bidford-on-Avon, Warwickshire, B50 4JH.

For further information or to place an order, telephone (01386) 870825 / 792755 or fax. (01386) 870825.

Student guide

We suggest you read this guide carefully before you begin any of the worksheets.

We advise you to keep all your worksheets in a folder.
You can then use them as a revision aid.

It would help to keep this guide in your folder too. As you work through the worksheets, you will probably want to refer to the guide to remind you of terms like adverb, adjective etc.

If you don't know the meaning of a word in a worksheet, use a dictionary to look up the word.
Sometimes the dictionary explanation of a meaning can be difficult to follow so look up the meaning in another dictionary. If you still don't understand, ask your tutor for help.

A good dictionary will also show how you can use a word, for example, whether a word can be used as an adjective.

You will need to be able to refer to a thesaurus for some of these worksheets.
A dictionary type thesaurus arranged in alphabetical order is easy to use and allows you to find alternatives for a particular word.

Remember, some of the alternatives in a thesaurus may not necessarily be suitable for your writing situation. For example, the thesaurus may give a slang word which wouldn't be appropriate in a piece of formal writing. If you are uncertain about any of the alternatives offered, you can check them in a dictionary.

You will find it useful to refer to these explanations as we use these words in some of the worksheets.

sentence - A sentence has at least one subject and one verb, and makes sense.

subject - This is what a sentence is about - someone, something or somewhere. Every sentence needs a subject.

verb - A verb is a word of action. Every sentence needs a verb which shows when an action happens.

Student guide

noun - A noun is a naming word. It can be the name of a person, place or thing.

adjective - An adjective is a descriptive word. Adjectives describe or give more information about nouns.

adverb - An adverb describes or gives more information about a verb.

phrase - A phrase is a group of words that does not make sense by itself. You can add a phrase or phrases to a sentence to include more information.

aside - An aside is a group of words which provides some additional information but isn't essential to the main meaning of a sentence.

Remember.

A word like 'shattered' can be a verb or an adjective depending on how it is used in a sentence. This happens to many words so always look at a word within a sentence and decide what role it plays in that particular sentence. You can always check in a good dictionary to see if a word can be used for that purpose.

You can use the answer section to check your work.

In some activities there are definite answers and you can check you are correct. In other activities you will often make different choices from us, but you may find our suggestions give you ideas for extending sentences or using different vocabulary.

At times we advise you to check your ideas with your tutor. If you are ever uncertain about an activity, explanation or answer, ask your tutor for help.

We give you advice about developing your writing.

Get into the habit of:

> planning,
> making a first draft,
> checking
> and rewriting

any piece of writing that is important. The more you practise using the ideas in these worksheets, the more confident you will become.

You can follow our advice about developing your writing when you are writing for other subject areas.

Check out your sentences

There are three sentences on the card below.

He always drives carefully.

What time is it?

Move out of the way!

 ## Activity 1

Now consider what you know about sentences. Write your answers to the questions about sentences in the boxes below.

1. You can use one of three punctuation marks at the end of a sentence. What are these three marks?
 	
   a)
 	
   b)
 	
   c)

2. What must the first word of a sentence always begin with?
3. What must a sentence always do?

4. A sentence must always contain two things. What are these?
 	
   a)
 	
   b)

You will find our ideas and explanations in the Answers. Discuss with your tutor any points that you don't understand or are uncertain about.

You have now seen what a sentence is, but you may not feel totally confident about all aspects of writing sentences.

Check out your sentences

Activity 2

Complete the grid below. Think carefully about the points and any comments you have been given about your writing. Beside each point, tick the appropriate column.

	I am confident	I need to practise	I need more help
Know how to use sentence punctuation:			
a) full stops			
b) question marks			
c) exclamation marks			
d) capital letters			
Understand:			
a) why a sentence needs a subject			
b) the part verbs play in sentences			
Write in sentences			
Use sentence checks			

If you feel:

► you need more help or practise in writing sentences, discuss this with your tutor. You may also find it helpful to work through parts of '*Sentence Sense*' - the previous book in this series.

► uncertain about using sentence checks, you are given help with this in '*Building on the foundations*' on pages **8** & **9**.

► confident about the aspects of writing sentences shown in the grid above, you are ready to move on to considering ways of improving your sentence style.

Building on the foundations

> ### The customer complained to the supervisor.

This is a simple sentence.

It is a sentence because it:

* makes **sense**
* has a **subject** - is about someone, something, somewhere
  (The subject is 'The customer'.)
* has a **verb** - something happens; an action takes place
  (The verb is 'complained'.)

This is also a simple sentence.

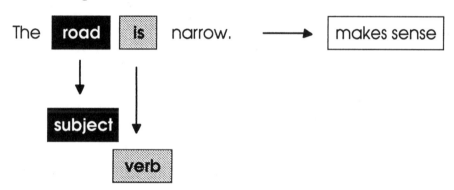

For your reader to understand exactly what you mean, you should write in sentences. This is important so always carry out the 3 sentence checks on the sentences you write.

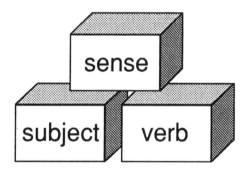

Read this passage.

> Jason and Emma bought a dog. It was a golden retriever. They called him Harley. He soon settled into his new home. Harley liked to play with the two kittens. The kittens did not like Harley. They hid from him.

Building on the foundations

▶ You probably thought this passage was boring. It sounds as if it was written for a young child. It is jerky and there is no 'flow' to it.

▶ It is written correctly in sentences but each sentence is a short, simple sentence.

Review

This book will:
- help you to develop the simple sentences you use as a foundation for your writing.
- show you a variety of ways to join, build up or extend sentences so that you feel happy using a variety of sentence structures.
- help you to punctuate your sentences correctly.

Example

The crowd cheered the team.

This simple sentence can be made more detailed and interesting by adding some descriptive words.

The excited crowd enthusiastically cheered the local football team.

Example

My sister works at Richley Hospital.
She looks after premature babies.

These two simple sentences can be joined in a number of ways to form one more flowing sentence.

My sister works at Richley Hospital and looks after premature babies.

My sister works at Richley Hospital where she looks after premature babies.

My sister who works at Richley Hospital looks after premature babies.

My sister works at Richley Hospital looking after premature babies.

Activity 1

Go back to the passage at the bottom of page **8**. See if you can:

         * add any describing words

         * join some of the sentences together

to improve the passage. Look again at the examples above to help you.

Being descriptive

Read the sentences in **Boxes A & B**.
Which sentences give you a clearer picture?

Box A

Protestors halted the procession.

The pop-star thrilled the fans.

Citizens hid in the buildings.

Box B

Furious protestors halted the peaceful procession.

The famous pop-star thrilled the cheering fans.

Terrified citizens hid in the shattered buildings.

▶ All the sentences give us some information but the sentences in **Box B** are more descriptive and interesting.

▶ Descriptive words have been added to the simple sentences in **Box A**. These descriptive words are called **adjectives**.

 ## Activity 1
By the side of each adjective below, write the word it describes in the sentence in **Box B** above. The first one is done for you.

Box C	Box D
Adjective	**Word it describes**
furious	protesters
peaceful	
famous	
cheering	
terrified	
shattered	

▶ The words adjectives describe are called **nouns**. These are naming words - the **names** of people, places or things. The words you have written in **Box D** are all nouns.

▶ We use the terms adjectives and nouns in this book but it isn't essential for you to use these words. The important thing is to remember to use adjectives when your writing needs to be vivid and descriptive.

Being descriptive

Activity 2

These are all adjectives.

huge	frayed	silent	sparkling	antique
damaged	enterprising	silver	calmer	red

Choose a suitable adjective to describe each noun written in bold print in the sentences below.

You may use any adjective from the box above or you may choose your own adjectives. Don't use the same adjective more than once.

a) A _____ **frost** covered the grass.

b) The _____ **ferry** reached _____ **waters.**

c) A _____ **cake** stood on a _____ **stand.**

d) The _____ **speed-boat** roared across the _____ **bay.**

e) _____ **youngsters** boosted the school funds.

f) The _____ **clock** was partly covered by a _____ **cloth.**

Activity 3

Think of a suitable adjective to describe each of these nouns. Use a different adjective for each noun.

Adjective	Noun	Adjective	Noun
	postman		student
	river		assignment
	table		plans
	curtain		aircraft
	councillor		city

Using several adjectives

When you describe

someone

something

somewhere

you may feel it is appropriate to use more than one adjective.

Examples

The **fresh, crisp, green** apple was just waiting to be eaten.

(These adjectives describe the noun 'apple'.)

The culprit was **thin, tall** and **well-dressed**.

(These adjectives describe the noun 'culprit'.)

▶ You will notice that in the first sentence the adjectives are placed in front of the noun they describe.

▶ In the second sentence the adjectives appear after the noun they describe.

▶ You can use either pattern according to the sentences you write.

Commas , , ,

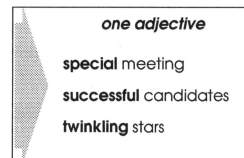

one adjective

special meeting

successful candidates

twinkling stars

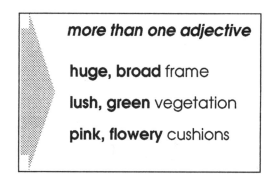

more than one adjective

huge, broad frame

lush, green vegetation

pink, flowery cushions

▶ You do not use a comma to separate an adjective from the noun it describes.

but

▶ You do use a comma to separate one adjective from another.

Using several adjectives

The day was **bright, sunny** but **cold**.

Darren is **pleasant, polite** and **likeable**.

The waiter isn't **friendly, welcoming** or **helpful**.

► Commas have been used to separate the adjectives in these sentences.
► You don't need a comma when you link adjectives with words like
'and', 'but', 'or'.

Activity 1
Put any missing adjectives and commas in these sentences.

a) The book I am reading is boring and _____ .

b) The _____ young recruits marched to the parade ground.

c) His writing was small _____ and clear.

d) The _____ visitors hurried to view the exotic rare birds.

e) Elaine fondled the fur of her glossy _____ cat.

f) The delayed passengers were tired _____ and angry.

Activity 2
Use each of these groups of words in a separate sentence. Remember to separate adjectives with commas where necessary.

a) strict demanding but fair   **d)** silent anxious parents

b) vast deserted beach   **e)** new expensive houses

c) careful accurate and detailed   **f)** large ruined castle

---

Review

♦ It sometimes helps to use a list of adjectives when you want to be descriptive or informative.

♦ Separate the adjectives with commas unless you separate them with:

and   **but**   **or**

Choosing adjectives

These can all be adjectives.

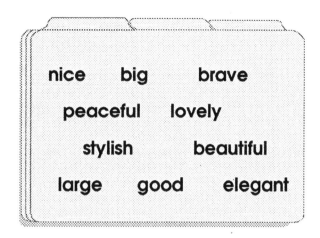

nice   big   brave

peaceful   lovely

stylish   beautiful

large   good   elegant

►   **nice**   **big**   **large**   **good**   **lovely**   **beautiful**
are probably the adjectives from the list above we use most.

There are plenty of adjectives we could choose to give a clearer, more detailed picture.

Example

This is a **nice** book.		Is it a **nice** book because it is:

          interesting   exciting
          informative   amusing
          entertaining   compelling

Activity 1

All the adjectives in **Box A** below could be used in the sentence in **Box A** instead of '**nice**'. They would give us a more exact picture of the day.

In **Box B** write down all the words that could replace '**horrid**' to give you a clearer picture of the weather.

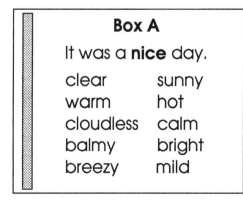

Box A

It was a **nice** day.

clear	sunny
warm	hot
cloudless	calm
balmy	bright
breezy	mild

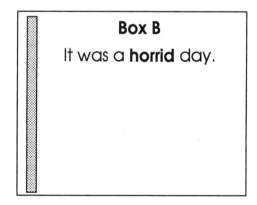

Box B

It was a **horrid** day.

Choosing adjectives

Activity 2

Use a thesaurus to find 2 adjectives that you could use in place of each of the adjectives in bold type below. (The adjectives you choose must fit the situation.) Avoid using any chatty, conversational adjectives or ones you don't understand.

Example When replacing 'delicious', don't choose chatty adjectives like 'yummy' or 'scrummy', or 'ambrosial' that you may not fully understand.

a **cheap** present	
a **clever** answer	
a **delicious** meal	
a **tidy** office	
a **calm** sea	
a **sad** expression	

Activity 3

Use each pair of adjectives in a separate sentence. Check each sentence you write. Can you improve it?

     a) kind   thoughtful   **d)** bitter   furious
     b) unwise   ill-considered   **e)** sour   vinegary
     c) inaccurate   thoughtless   **f)** tiring   demanding

Choosing verbs

Pages **10 - 15** are all about the importance of using and choosing adjectives to make your writing more detailed and descriptive.
In this unit we consider the importance of choosing verbs.

Example

The rude, surly waitress **looked** at the customer.

The verb in this sentence is **looked**

Remember ⟶ a verb shows an action is happening

⟶ every sentence needs a verb

We could have chosen our verb **'looked'** more carefully so that it was more descriptive too.

Examples

> glared
> glowered
> scowled

► Each of these verbs fits in with the adjectives and the whole sentence now gives us a more detailed picture.

The rude, surly waitress scowled at the customer.

Activity 1

Replace the verb given in bold type in each of these sentences with a more descriptive verb that fits the sentence. (You may use a thesaurus to help you.)

    a) A frightened holidaymaker **asked** for help.

    b) The angry, sulky pupil **walked** out of the room.

    c) The spoilt, demanding child **spoke** to her mother.

    d) The boy with the injured leg **went** out of the room.

    e) Susie's lazy son **sat** in the chair watching television.

    f) The prison officer **took** the prisoner to hospital.

More than one verb

On page **16** you saw that we use a verb to show that an action is happening.

Examples of verbs

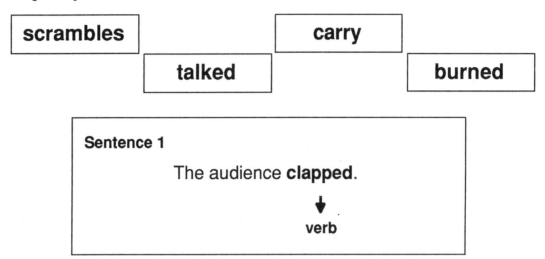

scrambles   carry   talked   burned

Sentence 1

The audience **clapped**.

↓

verb

► There is **one** action happening in **Sentence 1**.
► If you want to give the reader a more vivid and detailed account, you can include more than one verb in a sentence.

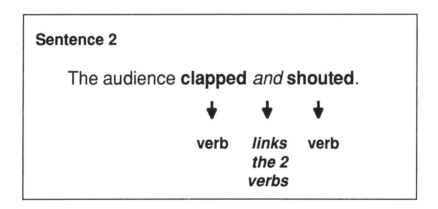

Sentence 2

The audience **clapped** *and* **shouted**.

↓   ↓   ↓

verb   *links*   verb
        the 2
        verbs

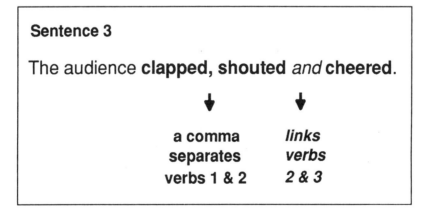

Sentence 3

The audience **clapped, shouted** *and* **cheered**.

↓   ↓

a comma   *links*
separates   *verbs*
verbs 1 & 2   *2 & 3*

You can see that **Sentence 3** has a greater impact than **Sentence 1**. It gives a more detailed picture of the audience's actions.

More than one verb

Activity 1
Make each of the sentences below more vivid and detailed by adding **one** other verb to sentences **a**, **b**, **c**, and **two** verbs to sentences **d**, **e**, **f**. Remember to add commas in the last three sentences.

a) He washed his new car.

b) Gill swims everyday.

c) The trapped animal trembled.

d) The children were running.

e) The crowd pushed through the doors.

f) The intruder kicked the elderly man.

Activity 2
Choose a suitable verb to put in each space and then use each group of verbs in a separate sentence. Remember to include commas where necessary.

a) swore _____ and threatened

b) crackled and _____

c) braked _____ and stopped

d) rode _____ and fished

e) cringed _____ and cowered

Describing actions

He walked.

► The sentence above tells us that someone walked. This may be all the information we need to give the reader, but sometimes we want to give a clearer or more descriptive picture.

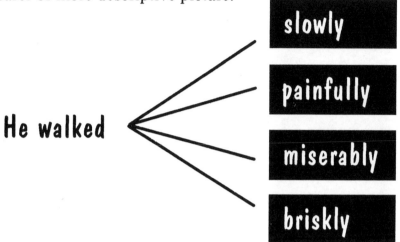

He walked
- slowly
- painfully
- miserably
- briskly

► The words shown in white type above are all adverbs. They describe the verb.

► Adverbs often show **how, when** or **where** an action happens. They add detail to the action.

Examples

He **carefully** climbed the ladder. (how)
Donna answered the door **immediately**. (when)
Savita searched **everywhere**. (where)

► Many adverbs end in '**ly**'.

Examples

She arrived **punctually** for the interview.
The receptionist spoke **clearly** to the caller.

► As you can see in the examples above, the adverb can go before or after the verb it describes.

Activity 1

Put a suitable adverb in the space in each of the sentences below. The adverb should add interest and detail to the action.

a) She sang the sad song _____ .

b) The young boy scribbled _____ in his book.

c) The artist _____ sketched the stormy sea.

d) The plane rose _____ into the air.

e) Sheena wept _____ when she heard the tragic news.

Describing actions

▶ Sometimes you can give a clearer and more powerful picture by using more than one adverb in a sentence.

Examples

The employee complained **bitterly** and **forcefully**.
The soldiers fought **boldly**, **bravely** but **brutally**.

▶ A comma is needed in the second example to separate the first adverb from the second adverb in the list. No comma is needed before link words like '**and**' '**but**'.

Activity 2

In each row of the table below you are given a verb and a list of adverbs. Some of the adverbs in the list aren't suitable for that verb.

For each verb, choose two or three appropriate adverbs from the list. Write a separate sentence for each verb and the 2 or 3 adverbs you have chosen.

verb	adverbs
waited	anxiously patiently soundly heavily
spoke	dangerously slowly loudly carefully
fell	heavily briefly awkwardly quietly
crawled	weakly desperately happily clumsily
worked	quickly carelessly clearly gently
ran	furiously fast softly deeply
blew	noisily eagerly sadly abruptly

Review

♦ Use adverbs to create a more powerful image, but don't overuse them.

♦ Always think carefully about the adverb you choose. It should fit the situation.

♦ Remember
   if a link word separates adverbs, no comma is needed
   2 adverbs placed together need a comma between them.

More lists

You saw on:

pages **12** & **13** *'Using several adjectives'*
pages **17** & **18** *'More than one verb'*
pages **19** & **20** *'Describing actions'*

that when you use more than one adjective, verb or adverb together in a list, you separate them with commas.

1. Maria, Jo, Syed and Malcolm met at college.
2. She sliced the tomatoes, courgettes, aubergines and onions.
3. On their holiday they will be travelling by coach, train, boat and plane.
4. The nearest villages are Meare, High Ham, Ashcott and Compton Dundon.
5. The chemist, butcher, hairdresser and baker all objected to the new traffic proposals.

► In the sentences above commas have been used to separate a list of **people**, **places** or **things**.

Activity 1

Complete the table below. Enter the sentence number against the type of list and copy down the list.
The first one has been done for you.

Commas are used for lists of:	Sentence numbers	Lists
places	4	Meare, High Ham, Ashcott and Compton Dundon
people		
things		

More lists

Activity 2

Complete these sentences by putting:

   * a suitable word or words in each space. (Choose your words carefully. Each sentence should be sensible and interesting.)

   * commas where they are needed to separate the items in each list.

a) Matthew and Brian swam snorkelled surfed and
_____ .   (*a list of verbs*)
b) My father collects old stamps maps atlases and
_____ .   (*a list of things*)
c) You can travel by Eurostar to _____ Brussels Lille
   and Bruges.   (*a list of places*)
d) Directors _____ clients and suppliers all attended
   the Annual Dinner.   (*a list of people*)
e) A _____ bony hand reached towards the
   _____ bubbling casserole.   (*a list of adjectives*)
f) Clive works quickly _____ and enthusiastically.
                                                   (*a list of adverbs*)

Activity 3

Now write 6 sentences of your own.

Sentence 1 should contain a list of **verbs**; 2 a list of **things**, 3 a list of **places**, 4 a list of **people**, 5 a list of **adjectives** and 6 a list of **adverbs**.

Look at the sentences in **Activity 2** to help you with this.

More lists

Extra Points

♦ The items in a list don't have to be just single words as you
have seen so far.
They can be groups of words.
Examples
She prepared **garlic mushrooms in breadcrumbs, beef in
a wine sauce, potatoes in their jackets, cauliflower with
a cheese sauce** and **peach trifle with honey cream**.

His preparations for the competition involved **jogging in the
park, running up sand dunes, skipping in the gym** and
swimming in the sea.

♦ The same rule applies for the use of commas.
Each item in the list should be separated from the next item
by a comma.

Activity 4

* Find a suitable way of completing each blank space in these sentences.
Each blank space should contain a group of at least 3 words. (Look at the
examples above in '**Extra Points**' to help you.)
* In sentences **a** and **b** the commas have been included to separate the items.
You will need to include the commas in sentences **c**, **d** and **e**.
* Write your sentences on a separate sheet of paper.

a) Tomorrow I will go shopping, ask _____ , visit
_____ and finish _____ .

b) He wore his shirt with _____ , the old trousers
_____ and an anorak with
_____ to the tramps barbecue.

c) Tom promised his father he would tidy the room put
_____ empty _____ and clear
_____ before teatime.

d) To raise money for the sports hall we shall _____
_____ and _____ .

e) I remember playing _____ dancing
_____ and singing _____ .

Putting it into practice

▶ You have seen that one way you can improve your sentences is by making them more vivid and detailed.

▶ This worksheet enables you to practise
* the points you have been given about using adjectives, adverbs and verbs
* using a thesaurus and dictionary to find appropriate words
* writing well-constructed, interesting sentences.

 ## Activity 1
Read the situation given below.

> It is a cold, bleak winter's night. You are visiting friends in a strange city. Your train was delayed and it is now midnight. There are no taxis or buses to take you to your friends' house so you decide to walk. Very soon you find yourself in a maze of dark streets. Many of the buildings are empty and boarded up. You begin to feel more and more desperate as you realise that you are lost. Suddenly you hear soft footsteps behind you. A car door slams in the darkness ahead and then lights blaze from what appears to be a derelict factory. You are terrified.

Continue the story from this point. Choose your words carefully to create a picture of the setting you are in and the drama of the situation. Make your reader feel he or she is caught up in your fear. Use the **Checklists** below and on the next page to help you.

> ### Checklist 1
> **Step 1 - Planning**
> ✓ Think about how you could continue the story.
> Consider:
> setting the scene
> your feelings
> what happens.
>
> ✓ Note down your plan.

Putting it into practice

Checklist 2

Step 2 - Preparation

✓ Here are some suggestions for words you might use:

       verbs - scurry, quake, sprint, pursue
       adjectives - gloomy, icy, panicky
       adverbs - frantically, rapidly

✓ Use a thesaurus and dictionary to find and list other appropriate words.

Checklist 3

Step 3 - First draft

✓ Write a first draft of your piece of writing.
Remember to:
    * include the vivid, descriptive words you have listed
    * concentrate on how you can put these words together to make interesting sentences.

✓ Check your draft.
    * Is it written in sentences?
    * Can you improve any of your sentences? (You may need to look back at previous worksheets.)

Checklist 4

Step 4 - Final draft

✓ Write a final draft.

✓ Check this carefully. Pay particular attention to spelling and punctuation.

✓ Discuss your piece of writing with your tutor.

Obviously you won't always be writing descriptive pieces, however, you will also find it helpful to follow the steps in the **Checklists** for other writing tasks.

Putting it into practice

Activity 2

For this activity you will be concentrating on producing a detailed, exact piece of writing for a formal situation. Your choice of words will need to be suitable for that situation and reader.

```
THE SITUATION
Your school / college is thinking of introducing a
four term year.

The terms would follow this pattern
   Term 1: mid January - mid March
   Term 2: mid April - end of June
   Term 3: beginning of August - beginning of October
   Term 4: mid October - mid December


You have been asked to give your views in writing to
your course tutor.
```

Remember to use the steps in the **Checklists** we gave you on pages **24** and **25** of this worksheet to help you with this task.

Use the additional checks given below for the first draft of this piece of writing, and for other pieces of formal writing.

Checks for Formal Writing

First draft
This is a formal writing situation.
✓ Check words
* Have you used appropriate words for the situation and the reader?
* Are the words you used sufficiently precise to communicate your ideas?
✓ Check sentences
* Have you written in sentences?
* Can any sentences be improved?
* Are your sentences in the right order to present your ideas clearly and logically?

Where, when, how, why?

► You have already looked at adding descriptive words (adjectives and adverbs) to your writing.
► In this worksheet we will be looking at adding **phrases** to sentences to make them more precise and informative.
► A **phrase** is a groups of word.

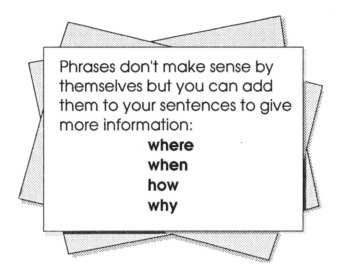

Phrases don't make sense by themselves but you can add them to your sentences to give more information:
where
when
how
why

Examples

for my sister (why)

I bought a present.

last week (when)

| I bought a present for my sister last week. |

or

| Last week I bought a present for my sister. |

She booked seats.   in Colchester (where)
by telephone (how)
for the performance (why)

| She booked seats by telephone for the performance in Colchester |

Where, when, how, why?

Activity 1

* Add the phrases given beside each sentence on page **29** and write down the longer sentence you have made.

* You may choose to add:
> a phrase at the beginning or end of a sentence
> one phrase after another.

* The place and order you choose to put the phrases in is important. Always check each sentence you've written to see if it:
> sounds right
> makes sense.

* We have done an example for you.

Sentence	Phrase
I go shopping.	each Saturday in the centre of Leeds

I go shopping in the centre of Leeds each Saturday.

You could also have chosen to write:

Each Saturday I go shopping in the centre of Leeds.

Where, when, how, why?

Sentences	Phrases
Thomas is celebrating his ninth birthday.	on Thursday by going to London
Garry bought a chocolate ice-cream.	for his friend during the interval
Seamus received a reply.	from his insurers within days
The exhausted dog went to sleep.	under the table after his walk across the fields
We stayed in Paris.	for the weekend on our anniversary
I will not finish my assignment.	for Mr Hughes until tomorrow

Extra Points

◆ Sometimes you will see a comma used after a phrase when the phrase is at the beginning of a sentence.
Example

In winter, the trees lose their leaves.
  * The writer is trying to stress this happens 'in winter'.
  * A comma has been used after 'winter' so that the reader pauses. This draws attention to the phrase '**in winter**'.
  * It would be equally correct to write the sentence without a comma. It depends on the effect you want to create.

◆ When you put a fairly long phrase at the beginning of a sentence, it is useful to use a comma after it. This helps to break up the sentence and makes it easier for the reader to understand.
Example

As part of your college course, you will be studying psychology.

◆ If you are uncertain about using a comma in this way, read the sentence aloud pausing at the comma to help you decide.

◆ Don't use a comma if it breaks up the natural flow of a sentence.

Asides

Paul Smith visited Bolton today.

► This sentence gives some information about Paul Smith - he visited Bolton today. However, you may wish to give some additional information about Paul Smith.

Paul Smith, **a well-known fashion designer**, visited Bolton today.

► The extra detail about Paul Smith is a **descriptive aside**.

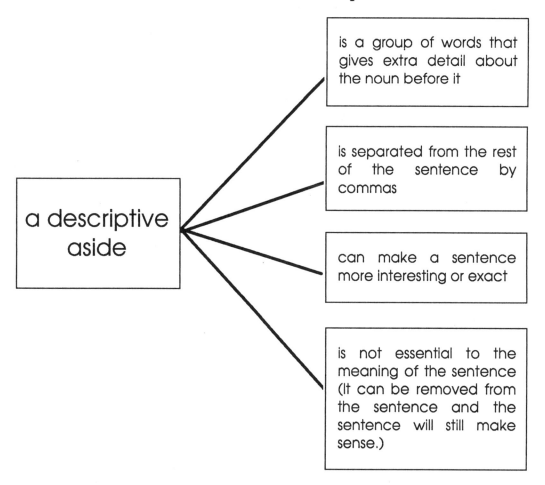

a descriptive aside

- is a group of words that gives extra detail about the noun before it
- is separated from the rest of the sentence by commas
- can make a sentence more interesting or exact
- is not essential to the meaning of the sentence (It can be removed from the sentence and the sentence will still make sense.)

Example

Birmingham, **a city with many canals,** is England's second city.

noun   comma   aside   comma

Birmingham is England's second city.

Without the aside, the sentence still makes sense.

Asides

Activity 1

Each of the sentences below contains a descriptive aside, but the commas which separate the aside from the rest of the sentence are missing.

Put in these missing commas. Check that you have put the commas in the correct places by writing out each sentence with the aside removed. Remember the sentence should still make sense.

a) My brother an architect works in London.

b) The car an old Mini lay rusting in the ditch.

c) Aftab driving a new BMW arrived before everyone else.

d) The office full of noisy people was the worst place to work.

e) John's home a small flat in Oxford has been for sale for two years now.

f) Our television company one of the largest in Europe wins at least one

award every year.

Review

◆ A descriptive aside gives extra detail and helps you to include more information within one sentence. Compare:
Example 1 - one sentence
    Our college, built in the 1960's, now needs many repairs.
Example 2 - two sentences
    Our college was built in the 1960's. It now needs many repairs.

◆ It allows you to vary your sentence style. For example, sometimes you can turn the sentence around and put the aside first.
Example
Sara, **looking tired and miserable**, said she would spend the rest
                    of the day in a hot bath.
Looking tired and miserable, Sara said she would spend the rest
                    of the day in a hot bath.

◆ If you start a sentence with an aside, check the sentence still sounds right and makes sense.

◆ When you put an aside at the beginning of a sentence, you need a comma after the aside.

Asides

Activity 2

Add a descriptive **aside** to each of the sentences below. The noun to which you will be adding extra details is shown in bold type. Remember the aside interrupts the sentence so put commas around it.

> **a)** My **cousin** has just returned from Mexico.
>
> **b)** **Robert** still walks five miles every day.
>
> **c)** The **cat** balanced on the high wall.
>
> **d)** Our local **school** might close next year.
>
> **e)** The **plane** carried 600 passengers.

Extra Points - other asides

▶ An aside has been included in each of the examples below. The aside is shown in bold type.

Examples

> **In my opinion,** you are wrong.
> His assignment was not acceptable, **unfortunately**.
> We are, **however,** able to offer a refund on this occasion.

▶ Such asides may:
* introduce a sentence
* give a comment
* interrupt a sentence.

Activity 3

You will notice that asides like those in **Extra Points** can come at the beginning, middle or end of a sentence. Look at the commas in each of the examples above and complete the following sentences.

> **a)** When an aside is at the beginning of a sentence, there is a
>
> comma... .
>
> **b)** When an aside is at the end of a sentence, there is a
>
> comma... .
>
> **c)** When an aside is in the middle of a sentence, there is a
>
> comma... .

These aren't asides

You saw on pages **30 - 32** '*Asides*' that when you add a non-essential piece of information to a sentence, you enclose it within commas.
Example

> **A young man, in his mid-twenties, was the only other occupant in the carriage.**

▶ Putting commas around the aside is like putting something in brackets to show it's less important.

▶ **'in his mid-twenties'** is part of the sentence and gives us some extra detail, but it is not essential to the main meaning of the sentence.

 Now read these sentences.

> 1. The house **next door** is for sale.
>
> 2. That essay **on her desk** is mine.
>
> 3. The yacht **in the harbour** is waiting to berth.
>
> 4. The girl **who has just entered the room** is Tom's girl friend.

Review

- The words in bold print in the sentences above don't have commas around them.
- They aren't asides.
- They are each an essential part of the sentence.
- They tell you exactly which place, person or thing is being talked about.
- It's like pointing at a particular item.

These aren't asides

Sometimes it's difficult to decide if you need commas. Look at the group of words and ask yourself:

Are these words essential to the meaning of the sentence? | YES |

Do they point out which one it is? | YES |

Are they just as important as the rest of the words in the sentence? | YES |

Remember the pattern for the comma checks.

Answer | YES | **NO** commas needed

Answer | NO | **YES**, commas needed

Activity 1

Now carry out the 3 checks for commas on these sentences. Some sentences will need commas, some won't.

> **a)** John my father's cousin won the team trophy.
>
> **b)** The hotel by the railway is being renovated.
>
> **c)** The glass on the display cabinet was difficult for Leroy to reach.
>
> **d)** The letter a copy of which was sent to the local newspaper announced his resignation.
>
> **e)** Peter Scott a sheep farmer from Mold was convicted of drunken driving.
>
> **f)** The table in the corner is solid mahogany.
>
> **g)** The woman dressed in green is my boss.
>
> **h)** The driver in the white Mercedes is travelling too fast.
>
> **i)** The shop at the end of the road is being demolished.

Linking sentences

The log sheet above was written by a student while he was on work experience. He wrote it during the day and just jotted down the sentences as he thought of them so the log is like a first draft of a piece of writing. It could be improved.

► You will have noticed that:

 there are a number of short jerky sentences
 in places the writing is rather stilted and doesn't flow.

Linking sentences

► Look at the log again. By linking some short sentences together, the writer could make the writing flow better and improve the style.

► Some of the sentences could be linked together with **'and'** because they are on the same topic and closely related.

Example A

The clothes are made in the factory. They are then sent to wholesale companies.

The clothes are made in the factory <u>and</u> then sent to wholesale companies.

► Other sentences are on the same topic but contrast with one another so could be linked with **'but'**.

Example B

Their clothing is mainly for women. They also make coats and trousers for children.

Their clothing is mainly for women, <u>but</u> they also make coats and trousers for children.

Review

♦ You may have noticed that sometimes you can omit words from the second sentence after linking it with **'and'** or **'but'**. In *Example A* above we left out 'they are' as these words aren't needed now the two sentences are linked together.

♦ In *Example B* above we put a comma before **'but'** to make the reader pause slightly. This pause helps to stress the contrast between the two items of information.

♦ You don't always have to use a comma before **'but'**, but it does draw attention to the contrast.

♦ Whenever you write a second draft, look for closely related or contrasting sentences and see if it would improve the style if you used **'and'** or **'but'** to link some of the sentences.

Linking sentences

Activity 1

Write a second draft of paragraphs 2 and 3 of the Work Experience Log on page **35**. Use the link words ('**and**' '**but**') to join any suitable sentences. Aim for a more fluent style.

Review

• You can use '**and**' or '**but**' to link short sentences together. By linking such sentences, you can improve the flow and style of your writing.

• So far in this worksheet, we have only shown two sentences linked together. You can link three sentences (and occasionally four sentences) together using '**and**', '**but**'.
Example
The team played well this Saturday **and** scored four goals, **but** last week they lost by six goals.

• Don't overuse '**and**'. If there are too many sentences linked together in this way, your writing can sound repetitive. In *'More sentence links'* on pages **38**, **39** we show you other ways of linking sentences.

Activity 2

Write two or three paragraphs about a company you have either worked at or visited on work experience.

STEPS

* Start by noting down your ideas.

* Write a first draft.

* Check your sentences to see if there are any closely related or contrasting sentences that would sound better linked.

* Are there any other improvements you could make?

* Write a second draft and then discuss this piece of writing with your tutor.

More sentence links

▶ On pages **35, 36, 37** you saw that **'and'** and **'but'** can be used to link sentences on the same topic.

▶ Although **'and'** and **'but'** work for some sentences, your writing could become repetitive if you only used this way of linking sentences. There are other words you can use to link sentences.

Other link words you could use:

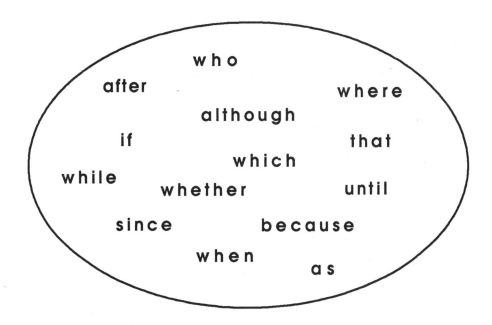

who
after
where
although
if
that
which
while
whether
until
since
because
when
as

▶ Each of the sentences in the examples below contains two ideas.
▶ Each idea could form a sentence, but the ideas have been joined together with a link word (**'after'**, **'while'**, **'although'**) to make one complete sentence.

Examples

1) I will finish my assignment **after** I have watched television.

2) Annette read a magazine **while** she waited for her interview.

3) The essay is satisfactory **although** you could have included more detail.

▶ Sometimes you can start the sentence with the link word.

Examples

4) After I have watched television, I will finish my assignment.

5) While she waited for her interview, Annette read a magazine.

6) Although you could have included more detail, the essay is satisfactory.

More sentences links

Activity 1

Choose link words from the circle on page **38** to join each pair of sentences below. Try to vary the pattern of your sentences by turning some around and starting with the link word.

Check each sentence you write to make sure it makes sense. If the link word comes at the beginning of the sentence, remember to include a comma.

a) He was made redundant. The company closed down.

b) The resource centre will have to close. The funding has been taken away.

c) The travellers waited for six hours. Their plane was repaired.

d) I still find Chester a fascinating city. I have visited it many times.

e) I will not be attending the dinner. I did not receive an invitation.

Activity 2

Follow the steps given below to write a paragraph or more about a place you know. This may be a town, a city, the countryside etc.

STEPS   * Make a list of ideas you could include.

   * Now think about which ideas you could link together.

   * Consider which link words you could use. (Look at the circle on page **38** and '*Linking sentences*' on pages **35**, **36** & **37**.)

   * When you have completed your first draft, check to see whether you can improve it.

Putting the links together

The swimming pool felt very cold **as** we jumped in **and** the shock certainly woke us up.

▶ In the sentence above we have used **two** link words **'as' 'and'** to combine **three** separate ideas on the same topic. These three ideas could each form a separate sentence.

Although the weather was bitterly cold, they decided to go out **because** the children were bored.

▶ **'although' 'because'** are used to link the ideas in this sentence.

Activity 1

* because we love the scenery	* if I apply now
* when the train came into the station	* after everyone had left
* after I have been to Israel	* and enjoy walking in the dales
* as there were no empty seats left	* because he liked working alone

Add two points from the box above to each of the sentences below. You should only use each idea once.

You may choose to add an idea to the beginning of a sentence. (If you do this, remember to include a comma.) Your completed sentence must make sense.

a) We shall go to Yorkshire this year for our holidays.

b) I shall be able to start my course in September.

c) Simon finished his work.

d) The passengers were furious.

Review

♦ You can use different link words to combine three or more ideas in a sentence.

♦ **But remember**, short sentences can also be effective.

♦ Aim for a variety of sentence patterns and lengths in any one piece of writing.

Using the skills

In the worksheets in this book you have:
* extended sentences by adding informative words and phrases
* used a variety of sentence styles.

Activity 1
Use these skills to help you write a precise formal letter for this situation.

> * You work for Leisureline - a company which manufactures sports equipment
> * Earlier today you phoned Ben Hurd - arranged for 2 members of staff, Harriet Kaufman & Keith Kelly, to attend conference in London - May 3rd & 4th
> * Your letter to Ben Hurd should confirm the points you made in your phone call:
>   * Harriet & Keith will attend
>   * They'll travel by train - arrive St Pancras 8.15pm night before
>   * Car will meet them - take them to Britannia Hotel
>   * Meal will be waiting for them - Harriet is vegetarian
>   * 8.30am first day of conference they'll meet Nazir Ahmed, conference organiser, in hotel reception
>   * Car has been arranged to take them from hotel to conference
>   * They'll bring 72 information packs (please contact if more needed)
>   * They'll give a presentation at conference - are planning it & will send outline at beginning of next week

ADVICE

be precise
include all the details
plan the best order for the information
use a business-like tone

Now write a first draft of your letter.

> **CHECKS**
>
> ✓ Have you given detailed, exact information?
> ✓ Are your sentences sufficiently varied?
> ✓ Are there any short sentences which could be linked together?
> ✓ Is your punctuation and spelling correct?

Now write a second draft of your letter making all the necessary improvements.

Answers

Check out your sentences   page 6
Activity 1
1 a) A sentence usually ends with a full stop.

b) A sentence which asks a question ends in a question mark.

c) It is also possible to end a sentence in an exclamation mark. This mark shows the reader that the sentence should be read with strong emotion.

2) Every sentence must begin with a capital letter.

3) A sentence must always make sense.

4 a) A sentence always has one or more subjects - the subject is what the sentence is about.

b) A sentence must contain at least one verb which shows that an action is happening and when it happens.

Building on the foundations   page 9
Activity 1
Here are our suggestions for you to consider. You will probably have chosen other ways so discuss your ideas with your tutor.

Jason and Emma bought a dog. It was a golden retriever which they called Harley. He soon settled into his new home where he liked to play with the two lively kittens. The kittens did not like the boisterous Harley and hid from him.

Being descriptive   pages 10 & 11
Activity 1
peaceful **procession**
famous **pop-star**
cheering **fans**
terrified **citizens**
shattered **buildings**

Activity 2
If you used the adjectives from the box, you may have made these choices.

a) A **sparkling** frost covered the grass.

b) The **damaged** ferry reached **calmer** waters.

c) A **huge** cake stood on a **silver** stand.

d) The **red** speed-boat roared across the **silent** bay.

e) **Enterprising** youngsters boosted the school funds.

f) The **antique** clock was partly covered by a **frayed** cloth.

Activity 3
Ask your tutor to check that you have chosen suitable adjectives.

Using several adjectives   page 13
Here are our suggestions for adjectives. You will probably have chosen different ones. You should have included commas as we have.

a) The book I am reading is boring and **difficult**.

b) The **eager,** young recruits marched to the parade ground.

c) His writing was small, **neat** and clear.

d) The **elderly** visitors hurried to view the exotic, rare birds.

e) Elaine fondled the fur of her glossy, **contented** cat.

f) The delayed passengers were tired, **hungry** and angry.

Activity 2
You will need to discuss your sentences with your tutor.

Choosing adjectives   pages 14 & 15
Activity 1
Here are some suggestions to describe the day more exactly. ·
rainy   windy   bleak   cold   freezing
cloudy   snowy   foggy   misty   damp   stormy

Activity 2
You may have chosen any of these words.
a **cheap** present
inexpensive   economical   low-cost
a **clever** answer
**intelligent   accurate   precise   detailed
knowledgeable   apt**
a **delicious** meal
tasty   mouthwatering   flavoursome
a **tidy** office
neat   orderly   uncluttered
a **calm** sea
tranquil   peaceful   smooth   placid
a **sad** expression
**unhappy   miserable   doleful   gloomy   glum
mournful   downcast**

Activity 3
Discuss your sentences with your tutor.

Choosing verbs   page 16
Activity 1
a) begged / pleaded for help.

b) ·**stormed / flounced** out of the room.

c) shouted / screamed at her mother.

d) limped / hobbled out of the room.

e) slumped / slouched / lounged in the chair

f) escorted the prisoner to hospital.

More than one verb   page 18
Activity 1
Here are our suggestions for verbs. You may have chosen different ones, but you should have included the commas as we have.

a) He washed **and polished** his new car.

b) Gill swims **and jogs** every day.

Answers

c) The trapped animal trembled **and shivered**.

d) The children were running, **shouting and screaming**.

e) The crowd pushed, **elbowed and jostled** through the doors.

f) The intruder kicked, **punched and shook** the elderly man.

Activity 2

Here are our suggestions for suitable verbs. Discuss your sentences with your tutor.

a) swore, **shouted** and threatened

b) crackled and **burnt**

c) braked, **swerved** and stopped

d) rode, **hunted** and fished

e) cringed, **whimpered** and cowered

Describing actions   pages 19 & 20

Activity 1

Here are our suggestions for suitable adverbs.

a) She sang the sad song **mournfully**.

b) The young boy scribbled **furiously** in his book.

c) The artist **hastily** sketched the stormy sea.

d) The plane rose **swiftly** into the air.

e) Sheena wept **bitterly** when she heard the tragic news.

Activity 2

We would have chosen these adverbs:

waited - **anxiously patiently**

spoke - **slowly loudly carefully**

fell - **heavily awkwardly**

crawled - **weakly desperately clumsily**

worked - **quickly carelessly**

ran - **fast furiously**

blew - **noisily eagerly**

Discuss your sentences with your tutor.

More lists   pages 21, 22 & 23

Activity 1

people	1	Maria, Jo, Syed and Malcolm
	5	chemist, butcher, hairdresser and baker
things	2	tomatoes, courgettes, aubergines and onions
	3	coach, train, boat and plane

Activity 2

Here are our suggestions. You may well have chosen different words, but you should have included the commas as we have.

a) Matthew and Brian swam, snorkelled, surfed and **sailed**.

b) My father collects old stamps, maps, atlases and **photographs**.

c) You can travel by Eurostar to **Paris**, Brussels, Lille and Bruges.

d) Directors, **staff,** clients and suppliers all attended the Annual Dinner.

e) A **thin,** bony hand reached towards the **hot,** bubbling casserole.

f) Clive works quickly, **carefully** and enthusiastically.

Activity 3

Discuss your sentences with your tutor.

Activity 4

Here are our suggestions. You probably made different choices. You should have included the commas as we have in **c**, **d**, **e**.

a) Tomorrow I will go shopping, ask **my brother for lunch**, visit **my best friend** and finish **planning my essay**.

b) He wore his shirt with **the buttons missing**, the old trousers **with a tear in the knee** and an anorak with **oil stains down the front** to the tramps' barbecue.

c) Tom promised his father he would tidy the room, put **his stamp collection away**, empty **all the rubbish from his drawers** and clear **the dining room table** before teatime.

d) To raise money for the sports hall, we shall **plan a sponsored bike ride, hold a pig roast** and **have a car boot sale**.

e) I remember playing **my brother's guitar**, dancing **with my friend's mum** and singing **all the way home**.

Putting it into practice   pages 24 & 26

Activities 1 & 2

Discuss each piece of writing with your tutor.

Where, when, how, why?   page 29

Activity 1

We would choose to add the phrases in these ways.

Thomas is celebrating his ninth birthday on Thursday by going to London.   **or**

Thomas is celebrating his ninth birthday by going to London on Thursday.   **or**

On Thursday, Thomas is celebrating his ninth birthday by going to London.

Garry bought a chocolate ice-cream for his friend during the interval.   **or**

During the interval, Garry bought a chocolate ice-cream for his friend.

Seamus received a reply from his insurers within days.   **or**

Within days, Seamus received a reply from his insurers.

The exhausted dog went to sleep under the table after his walk across the fields.   **or**

Answers

After his walk across the fields, the dog went to sleep under the table.

We stayed in Paris for the weekend on our anniversary.   **or**
On our anniversary, we stayed in Paris for the weekend.

I will not finish my assignment for Mr Hughes until tomorrow.

You will notice that where we have chosen to put one of the phrases at the beginning of a sentence, we have included a comma after the phrase. There is more about this on page **29** under '**Extra Points**'.

Asides   pages 31 & 32
Activity 1
a) My brother, an architect, works in London.
b) The car, an old Mini, lay rusting in the ditch.
c) Aftab, driving a new BMW, arrived before everyone else.
d) The office, full of noisy people, was the worst place to work.
e) John's home, a small flat in Oxford, has been for sale for two years now.
f) Our television company, one of the largest in Europe, wins at least one award every year.

Activity 2
Our suggestions for asides are shown below. You should have included commas as we have.
a) My cousin, **an intrepid explorer**, has just returned from Mexico.
b) Robert, **an elderly man in his eighties**, still walks five miles every day.
c) The cat, **trying to escape from the vicious dogs**, balanced on the high wall.
d) Our local school, **which has only ten pupils**, might close next year.
e) The plane, **one of the largest in the world**, carried 600 passengers.

Activity 3
a) When an aside is at the beginning of a sentence, there is a comma **after the aside**.
b) When an aside is at the end of a sentence, there is a comma **before the aside**.
c) When an aside is in the middle of a sentence, there is a comma **before the aside and a comma after the aside**.

These aren't asides   page 34
Activity 1
a) John, my father's cousin, won the team trophy.
b) The hotel by the railway is being renovated.
c) The glass on the display cabinet was difficult for Leroy to reach.

d) The letter, a copy of which was sent to the local newspaper, announced his resignation.
e) Peter Scott, a sheep farmer from Mold, was convicted of drunken driving.
f) The table in the corner is solid mahogany.
g) The woman dressed in green is my boss.
h) The driver in the white Mercedes is travelling too fast.
i) The shop at the end of the road is being demolished.

Linking sentences   page 37
Activity 1
Discuss your paragraphs with your tutor.

Activity 2
Discuss your writing with your tutor.

More Sentence Links   page 39
Activity 1
Our suggestions are:
a) He was made redundant **because** the company closed down.
b) **As** the funding has been taken away, the resource centre will have to close.
c) The travellers waited for six hours **while** their plane was repaired.
d) I still find Chester a fascinating city **although** I have visited it many times.
e) **Since** I did not receive an invitation, I will not be attending the dinner.
You may have chosen other link words or linked the sentences in other ways so discuss your sentences with your tutor.

Activity 2
Discuss your writing with your tutor.

Putting the links together   page 40
Activity 1
We would choose to link the ideas in these ways.
a) We shall go to Yorkshire this year for our holidays because we love the scenery and enjoy walking in the dales.
b) If I apply now, I shall be able to start my course in September after I have been to Israel.
c) Simon finished his work after everyone had left because he liked working alone.
d) When the train came into the station, the passengers were furious as there were no empty seats left.
Discuss your sentences with your tutor.

Using the skills   page 41
Activity 1
Discuss your letter with your tutor.